This series of practice papers is intended to strengthen your understanding of the topics covered in the Programme of Study for Key Stage 3 Science. It will help you to prepare for the two National Curriculum Tests in Science, which you will undertake at the end of Year 9.

There are three sets of practice papers in this book (six papers in total). You will find the mark schemes in a separate section inserted at the centre.

These practice papers have been designed to perfectly reflect the style and format of the questions in the National Curriculum Tests. They are a useful resource and invaluable revision aid that will help to boost your confidence and reinforce your learning in the build up to your exams.

Each National Curriculum Test in Science will last for one hour and these practice papers have been designed to take roughly the same length of time. However, I would suggest that you try to complete each practice test, no matter how long it takes, to enable you to get the most from each paper. The papers cover all the aspects of the science curriculum that will be tested, including:

• cells and cell functions, nutrition, respiration, and health
• solids, liquids and gases, elements, compounds and mixtures, chemical reactions, geological changes and metals
• physical processes such as electricity and magnetism, forces and motion, light and sound, and the solar system

Everything on the Programme of Study for Key Stage 3 is covered in our bestselling revision guide, The Essentials of Key Stage 3 Science.

Practice papers for Tier 3-6 are also available.

Good luck in your tests.

Katie Whelan

© 2005 Lonsdale Revision Guides. All rights reserved. No part of this publication may be reproduced, stored in a retrieval system, or transmitted in any form or by any means, Electronic, Mechanical, Photocopying, Recording, or otherwise without the prior written permission of Lonsdale Revision Guides.

Lonsdale

Sc

KEY STAGE
3

TIER
5- 7

Science test

Paper 1A

Please read this page carefully but do not open the booklet until you are told to start. Write your name and the name of your school in the spaces below.

First name ______________________

Last name ______________________

School name ______________________

Remember

- The test is 1 hour long.
- You should have the following things on your desk: pen, pencil, rubber, ruler, protractor and calculator.
- The easier questions are at the beginning of the test.
- Try your best to answer all of the questions.
- The marks available for each question are shown below the mark boxes at the side of each question.
- Do not use rough paper. Write your answers and any working on the paper itself.
- Don't forget to check your work carefully.
- Ask your teacher if you are unsure about anything.

Total marks	

For marker's use only

Lonsdale

1. (a) Hefin and Ian were looking at cells under the microscope. They thought that they were looking at plant cells because of the following reasons. Indicate whether the statements were true or false by placing a 'T' or an 'F' in the boxes alongside.

"There is a membrane so it's a plant cell." ☐

"We can't see a nucleus so it's a plant cell." ☐

"There are chloroplasts so it's a plant cell." ☑

"It must be a plant cell because it has cytoplasm." ☐

(b) Hefin and Ian added iodine to the material under the microscope and it changed colour from pale brown to blue-black.

(i) What does this colour change indicate?

Red

(ii) Does this support their claim that they were looking at plant cells?

_____

(c) Name two types of specialised plant cells.

1 _____

2 _____

(d) Name two types of specialised animal cells.

1 _____

2 _____

Maximum 6 marks

1a | 2 marks

1bi | 1 mark

1bii | 1 mark

1c | 1 mark

1d | 1 mark

2. Grace and Katie measured the heights of people in their class and produced the following bar chart.

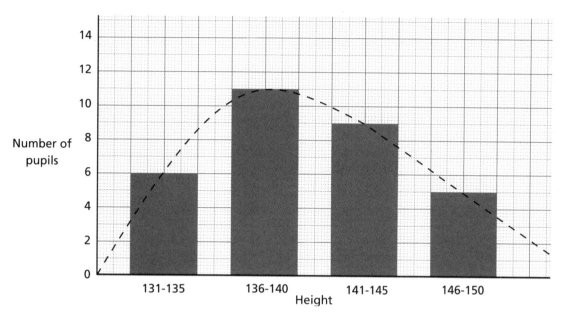

(a)(i) What units of measurement were used to measure the height of the class?

Centimeter centimetre

2ai

1 mark

(ii) How many people were in the 146-150 range?

_5._

2aii

1 mark

(iii) How many people were in the class?

_31_

2aiii

1 mark

(b) The dotted line shows the overall shape of their bar chart. If they investigated the following characteristics, which would produce a similar shape to the first bar chart?

(i) Weight ☑

(ii) Eye colour ☐

(iii) Intelligence ☐

(iv) Hair colour ☐

2b

2 marks

(c) Weight is a characteristic which:

(i) Depends totally on inherited factors ☐

(ii) Depends totally on environmental factors ☐

(iii) Depends on both inherited and environmental factors ☑

2c

1 mark

Maximum 6 marks

5

3. (a) Beverley and Paul left a box of toys on the lawn for a few days and when they moved the box they were astonished to find that the grass underneath had turned yellow.

    (i) What substance causes the green colour in plants?

    _____

    (ii) Why was this substance missing from the grass which had been under the toy box?

    _____

    (iii) Explain what would happen to the yellow grass over the next few days.

    _____

    _____

    (b) Paul suggested that a clear plastic sheet would have the same effect, so he pegged it onto the lawn and left it for a few days.

    (i) Would you expect the grass to become yellow?

    _____

    (ii) Explain your answer to (i) above.

    _____

    (c) What is the name of the process by which green plants make glucose using the energy from the sun?

    _____

Maximum 6 marks

3ai — 1 mark
3aii — 1 mark
3aiii — 1 mark
3bi — 1 mark
3bii — 1 mark
3c — 1 mark

4.   Elliott holds a ball at the top of a ramp.

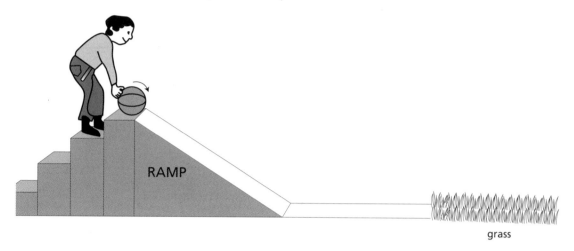

RAMP

grass

(a)   What type of energy does the ball have when it is at the top of the ramp?

gravitational potential energy

4a

1 mark

(b)   What type of energy is this converted to when the ball is rolling down
        the ramp?

Movement energy

4b

1 mark

(c)   Elliott lets the ball roll down the ramp. What force is acting on it to cause it to
        roll down the ramp?

gravity

4c

1 mark

(d)   When the ball meets the ground it is travelling 2m/s. If the ball continues to
        travel at the same speed, how far will it travel in 4 seconds?

8 metres

4d

1 mark

(e)   The ball then rolls over some grass. What happens to its speed and why?

its speed would decrease because friction is increased
from the grass

4e

2 marks

Maximum 6 marks

5.   The diagram below shows a simple circuit that Sam has connected.

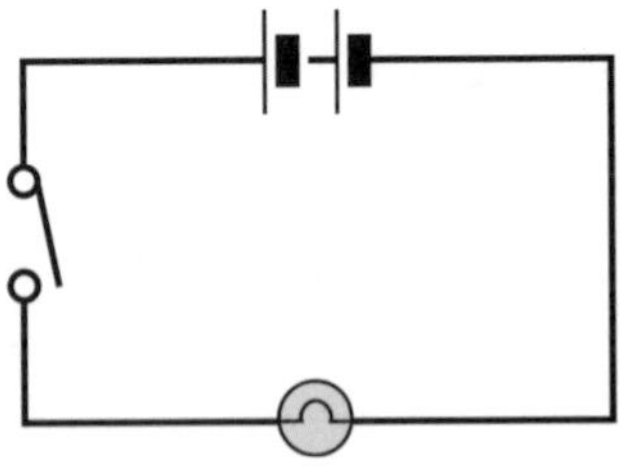

(a)   What does Sam need to do in order to turn the bulb on?

close the switch

5a
1 mark

(b)   Sam inserts another bulb into the circuit, as shown in the diagram below.

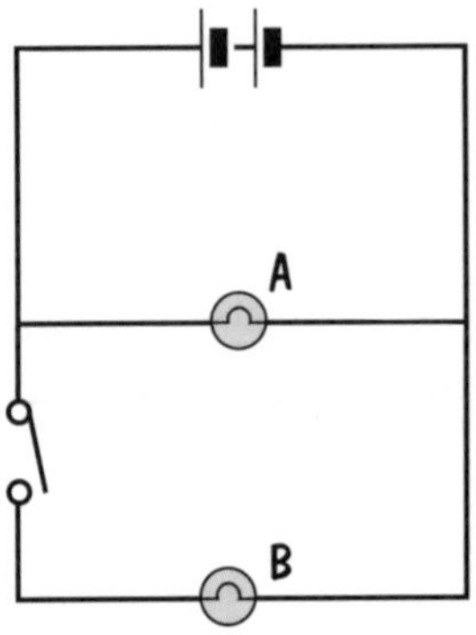

A

B

(i)   Is the new circuit a series or a parallel circuit?

Parallel circuit

5bi
1 mark

(ii)   Put a tick in the boxes next to the statements that are true for this circuit.

Both bulbs will be on all the time ☐

Bulb A will be on all the time ☑

Bulb B will be on all the time ☐

Bulb B will be on only when the switch is closed ☑

Both bulbs will be off all the time ☐

5bii
2 marks

(iii)   If 0.4 amps flows from the cell in the circuit on part (b), how many amps would flow through each of the two bulbs, assuming they were identical bulbs?

0.2 Amps

5biii
2 marks

Maximum 6 marks

6.   Look at the diagram below.

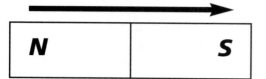   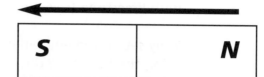

N	S

S	N

(a)   If the magnets are brought close together, will they attract or repel each other?

repel

6a

1 mark

(b)   Insert the words below into the gaps in the following sentences.

iron   **South**   **magnetic field**   **North**   **plastic**

Magnets have a region of space around them called a *magnetic field*.

They have two poles, which are *North* and *South* .

They can attract magnetic materials. One magnetic material is *iron* .

Magnets have no effect on non-magnetic materials, such as *plastic* .

6b

5 marks

Maximum 6 marks

7. Grace and Imogen performed an investigation into how different acids react with limestone (calcium carbonate).

They set up the equipment as shown and then conducted several experiments using the following different acids: vinegar, lemon juice, dilute hydrochloric acid and dilute sulphuric acid.

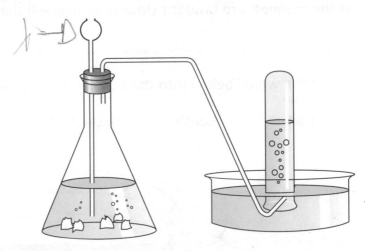

(a) Label with an X the piece of apparatus through which the acid is added.

(b) What is being measured in this experiment?

The amount of gas produced for is being Measured

(c) Describe one piece of evidence which tells you that a chemical reaction is occurring.

rise in temperature

(d) Name two things which would have to be kept constant in order to make this a fair test.

1 amount of limestone

2 amount of acid

(e) Name a gas which dissolves in rain to make it acidic.

carbon dioxide

Maximum 6 marks

8. James and Thomas carried out an experiment to investigate how the solubility of sugar changes with temperature. Sugar was added to the water until no more dissolved.

Temperature of water (°C)	Amount of sugar dissolved (g)
0	0
10	15
20	31
30	45
40	60
50	76
60	93

(a) Plot these results on the graph paper below.

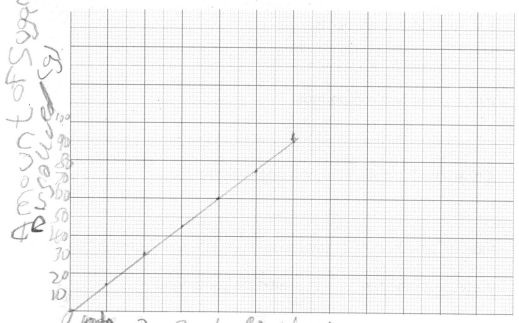

(b) Why did no sugar dissolve at 0°C?

because the water would have been frozen

(c) How much sugar would dissolve at 35°C?

51g

(d) Which substance in this experiment was the solvent?

water

Maximum 6 marks

8a
3 marks

8b
1 mark

8c
1 mark

8d
1 mark

9.   Look at the following diagrams that represent chemical particles.

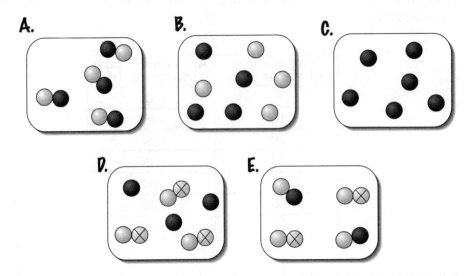

A.   B.   C.   D.   E.

(a) Write down the letter of the diagrams that represent the following:
(i) a mixture of two elements.

_B_____

9ai
1 mark

(ii) a mixture of two compounds.

_E_____

9aii
1 mark

(iii) a mixture of one element and one compound.

_D_____

9aiii
1 mark

(b) Indicate whether the following substances are mixtures or compounds.

(i) Water from the tap   ~~mixture~~/compound

9bi
1 mark

(ii) Cup of coffee   mixture/~~compound~~

9bii
1 mark

(iii) Lemonade   mixture/~~compound~~

9biii
1 mark

Maximum 6 marks

12

10. (a) Phoebe decides to
experiment with green and
red filters and her torch.

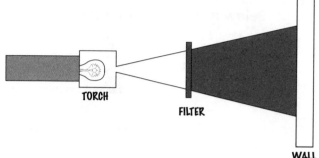

TORCH

FILTER

WALL

(i) She shines the torchlight through the green filter. What colour will the wall
appear to be?

_____green_____

10ai

1 mark

(ii) She then puts the red filter behind the green filter and shines the torch again.
Explain what will happen to the light.

No lit

10aii

1 mark

(iii) She cuts a square out of the middle of the red filter and puts both filters in
front of the torch. What will she see on the wall now?

A green squre

10aiii

1 mark

(b) Phoebe then shines the light through the green filter onto her red jumper.

(i) What colour will her jumper appear to be?

black

10bi

1 mark

(ii) Explain why.

only green light will fall your her jumper
and this will all be absorbed

10bii

1 mark

(iii) What colour will her jumper appear to be if she shines light onto it through the
red filter?

red

10biii

1 mark

Maximum 6 marks

11. Below is a diagram of a see-saw.

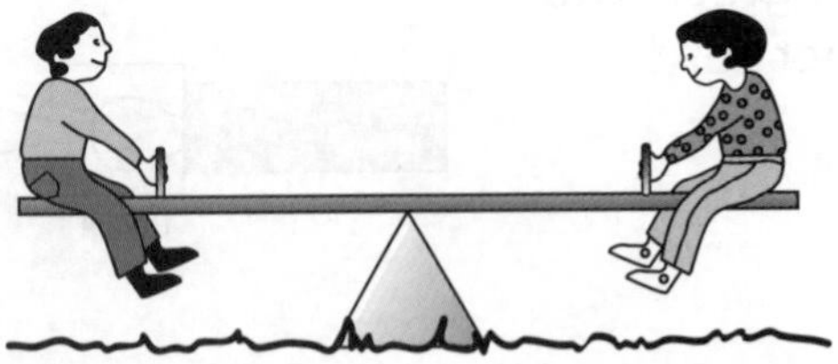

There are five children who want to play on the see-saw.
Opposite is a table of their weights

Child's name	Weight in N
Simone	450
Patrick	500
Omar	500
Abigail	400
Colin	550

(a) What are the names of the only two people who can make the see-saw balance if they sit equal distances from the pivot?

Omar

11a — 1 mark

(b) If Omar sits on the left of the see-saw and Colin sits an equal distance away on the right, the see-saw will tip.

(i) Who will be closest to the ground?

Colin

11bi — 1 marks

(ii) What is the direction of Omar's moment about the pivot - clockwise or anti-clockwise?

Clockwise

11bii — 1 marks

(c) If Colin sits 2 metres from the pivot, where will Abigail need to sit in order to counterbalance him?

2.75 from the pivot

11c — 1 mark

(d) If Colin and Omar sit together 4 metres from the pivot where would the others all need to sit together to counterbalance them?

[illegible] = ? [illegible]

Colin + Omar = 1050 × 4 = 4200

4200 ← [illegible] = 4200/1350 = 3.1m

11d — 2 marks

Maximum 6 marks

12. A group of students investigated how quickly different liquids evaporated. They set up the equipment as shown below.

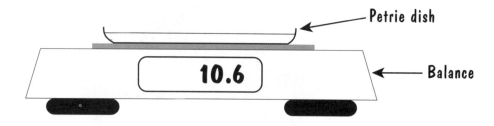

They put their results into the following table.

Liquid	Starting mass (g)	Mass after 24hrs (g)	Loss of mass (g)
A	10.6	8.4	2.2
B	12.5	10.1	2.4
C	11.2	10.7	0.5
D	10.8	9.3	1.5

(a) (i) Which liquid evaporated the quickest?

_A_

12ai

1 mark

(ii) Which liquid lost the greatest mass?

_B_

12aii

1 mark

(iii) What extra column would you add to the table to make the results more meaningful?

Percentage of liquid lost

12aiii

1 mark

(b) Name two variables which would have to be controlled in this experiment in order to make it a fair test.

1 _____

2 _____

12b

2 marks

(c) If the liquids had been ethanol, paraffin, petrol and water, which of the four liquids (A, B, C or D) is most likely to be water?

_C_

12c

1 mark

Maximum 6 marks

13.

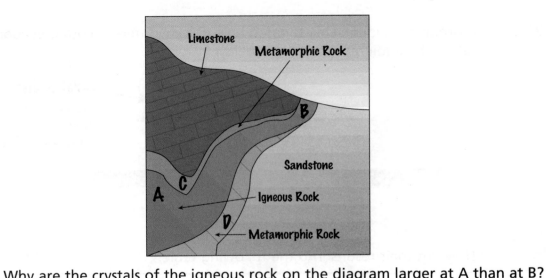

(a) Why are the crystals of the igneous rock on the diagram larger at A than at B?

_____

_____

(b) From which molten substance is igneous rock formed?

_____

(c) Why would different metamorphic rocks be formed at C and D?

_____

(d) How are sedimentary rocks formed?

formed from layers of sediment that from on top of each other these become compacted together to make a sandstone

(e) Give an example of a sedimentary rock.

limestone

Maximum 6 marks

14. (a) Hedgehogs, like many other mammals, hibernate in winter. What would you expect to happen to the following features of a hedgehog during hibernation?

(i) Its body mass.

decrease

14ai

1 mark

(ii) Its temperature.

decrease

14aii

1 mark

(iii) Its oxygen consumption.

decrease

14aiii

1 mark

(b) Deciduous trees also have a survival strategy to get them through the winter. Outline two features of this strategy.

1 _decreased cell activity_

2 _shedding leaves_

14b

2 marks

(c) Outline one other winter survival strategy which is used by birds.

migration

14c

1 mark

Maximum 6 marks

15. (a) The diagram below shows the relative thickness of the uterus lining over the course of the female monthly cycle.

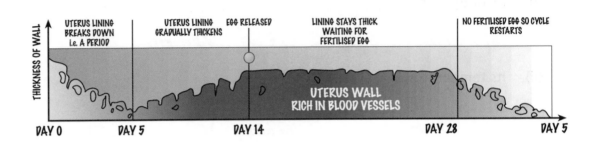

(i) For how long does the lining of the uterus continue to break down?

_____

15ai
1 mark

(ii) How long (in days) does the cycle last on average?

_____

15aii
1 mark

(iii) For how long (approximately) does the wall of the uterus remain at its thickest?

_____

15aiii
1 mark

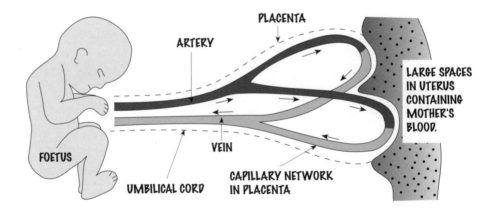

(b)(i) Oxygen and food pass from the mother to the baby. Which two substances travel in the opposite direction?

1_____

2_____

15bi
2 marks

(ii) Why is it important that a mother doesn't smoke during pregnancy?

_____

_____

Maximum 6 marks

15bii
1 mark

Sc

KEY STAGE
3

TIER
5- 7

Science test

Paper 2A

Please read this page carefully but do not open the booklet until you are told to start. Write your name and the name of your school in the spaces below.

First name ______________________

Last name ______________________

School name ______________________

Remember

- The test is 1 hour long.
- You should have the following things on your desk: pen, pencil, rubber, ruler, protractor and calculator.
- The easier questions are at the beginning of the test.
- Try your best to answer all of the questions.
- The marks available for each question are shown below the mark boxes at the side of each question.
- Do not use rough paper. Write your answers and any working on the paper itself.
- Don't forget to check your work carefully.
- Ask your teacher if you are unsure about anything.

Total marks	

For marker's use only

Lonsdale

1.   Diagrams of an animal cell and a plant cell are shown below.

ANIMAL CELL   PLANT CELL

(a)   Which part of the plant cell is non-living?

1a

1 mark

_____

(b)   Name two structures which are present in plant cells but not animal cells.

1 _____

1b

2 marks

2 _____

(c)   Which structure in both plant cells and animal cells controls the passage of substances into and out of the cell?

1c

1 mark

_____

(d)   In which structure in plant cells does photosynthesis take place?

1d

1 mark

_____

(e)   In which part of the cell is cell sap found?

1e

1 mark

_____

Maximum 6 marks

2.   Look at the animals drawn below.

John Dory   Zetek's Frog   Skylark

Common Iguana   Red Deer

(a)   To which large group do all these animals belong?

_____

2a
1 mark

(b)   Which one of the animals shown above is a mammal?

_____

2b
1 mark

(c)   Give two characteristics of mammals.

1 _____

2 _____

2c
2 marks

(d)   Which of the animals shown above breathes through its skin?

_____

2d
1 mark

(e)   Which one of the animals shown above has the lightest bones?

_____

2e
1 mark

Maximum 6 marks

3. Nearly a hundred years ago scientists were investigating the ways in which different food types contributed to obesity. They used a group of 30 volunteers who were given various different food types for a period of 3 months.

    Group A was given only foods which were high in fat.

    Group B was given only foods which were high in protein.

    Group C was given only foods which were high in carbohydrates.

    (a)(i) List three things the scientists would have to keep the same in order to make this a fair test.

    1 _____

    2 _____

    3 _____

3ai

3 marks

    (ii) Name the one factor that the scientists changed in this experiment (the independent variable).

    _____

3aii

1 mark

    (b) It was found that people on the high protein diet gained least weight. However, a diet consisting only of protein would not be good for you. Give two reasons why this is so.

    1 _____

    _____

    2 _____

    _____

3b

2 marks

    Maximum 6 marks

4. (a) A student set up the experiment as shown below to investigate the substances breathed out by humans.

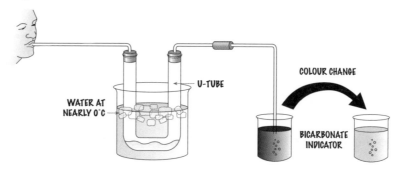

(i) What is the clear substance formed at the bottom of the U-tube?

_____

4ai

1 mark

(ii) What substance causes the bicarbonate indicator to change from purple to yellow?

_____

4aii

1 mark

(b) The student then set up the following experiment using seeds.

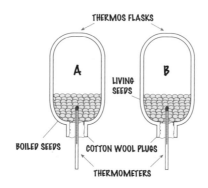

(i) What would you expect to notice about the temperature of the two flasks after 48 hours?

_____

4bi

1 mark

(ii) What process would cause this to happen?

_____

4bii

1 mark

(iii) Would you expect this to occur in all living things?

Yes ☐   No ☐

4biii

1 mark

(iv) What units would be used to measure the temperature in the flasks?

_____

4biv

1 mark

Maximum 6 marks

5. (a) Railway lines have gaps between neighbouring sections of track. These gaps are about 10mm wide.

(i) How does the size of objects change as they get hotter?

_____

5ai

1 mark

(ii) As the temperature of the railway line increases, what happens to the gaps between the neighbouring sections of track?

_____

5aii

1 mark

(iii) What problem would be caused by a rise in temperature if there were no gaps between sections?

_____

5aiii

1 mark

(iv) In countries which experience larger variations in temperature, should the gaps be wider or narrower?

_____

5aiv

1 mark

(b)(i) When a train driver applies his brakes, what is it that slows the train down?

_____

_____

5bi

1 mark

(ii) What effect does this process have on the temperature of the railway lines?

_____

_____

5bii

1 mark

Maximum 6 marks

6. Julie placed a conical flask onto a balance. It weighed 60g. She then added 100g of dilute hydrochloric acid and 5g of calcium carbonate. The total mass of the beaker, the acid and the calcium carbonate was therefore 165g at the start of the reaction.

165.00g

(a) How could Julie tell, by looking, that a chemical reaction was occurring?

_____

_____

6a

1 mark

(b) What would you expect to have happened to the total mass shown on the balance by the end of the reaction?

_____

_____

6b

1 mark

(c) Explain why you think this would have happened.

_____

_____

6c

1 mark

(d) What other change may have occurred in the beaker?

_____

_____

6d

1 mark

(e) Complete the word equation for this reaction.

Calcium carbonate + hydrochloric acid ⟶ ⬜ + ⬜ + ⬜

6e

1 mark

(f) Name a naturally occurring substance which is mainly compound of calcium carbonate.

_____

6f

1 mark

Maximum 6 marks

7. Peter and Maggie were investigating the reactivity of different metals by adding them to cold water and to hydrochloric acid. They recorded the following results:

Metal	Reaction with cold water	Reaction with dilute hydrochloric acid
Iron	Reacts with steam to produce a gas and iron oxide	Moderate reaction to produce bubbles of gas
Gold	No reaction	No reaction
Sodium	Floats, melts then seems to catch fire due to heat of reaction	Reacts explosively (SHOULD NEVER BE DONE!)
Magnesium	Very slow reaction to produce a gas and magnesium hydroxide	Reacts quickly to produce bubbles of gas

(a) List these metals in order of their reactivity, **starting with the most reactive.**

_____

_____

_____

_____

(b) Suggest another metal which isn't in this table that reacts in a similar way to sodium.

_____

(c) In the reactions above, where bubbles of gas are produced, which gas is given off?

_____

(d) Complete the word equation for the reaction between magnesium and dilute hydrochloric acid.

Magnesium + dilute hydrochloric acid ⟶ _____ + _____

(e) Besides bubbles of gas, what other evidence would indicate that a chemical reaction was occurring?

_____

(f) Why are reactive metals never found as pure metals but always as ores?

_____

_____

Maximum 6 marks

7a — 1 mark
7b — 1 mark
7c — 1 mark
7d — 1 mark
7e — 1 mark
7f — 1 mark

8. After it snowed Sunil and Ian went sledging on the hills. The diagram below shows their sledging route.

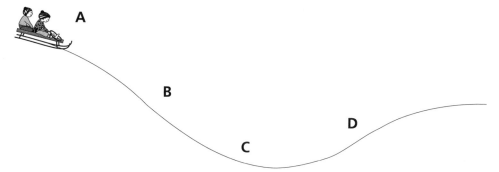

(a)(i) At which point would they be travelling fastest?

_____

8ai

1 mark

(ii) At which point would they be accelerating?

_____

8aii

1 mark

(iii) At which point would they be decelerating?

_____

8aiii

1 mark

(b)(i) Name two forces acting on the sledge at point B

1 _____

2 _____

8bi

2 marks

(ii) At point C these two forces are balanced. What can you say about their speed at this point?

_____

_____

8bii

1 mark

Maximum 6 marks

9. Some students were investigating the heating effects of different fuels. The fuels they chose were petrol, white spirit, ethanol and paraffin. They set up their equipment as shown in the diagram below.

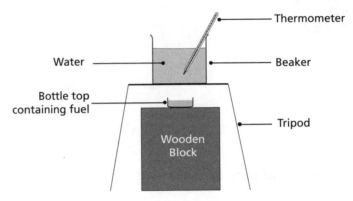

(a) List two things which would have to be kept the same in order to make this a fair test.

1_____

2_____

9a

2 marks

(b) Which is the independent variable (that is, the thing that is being measured)?

_____

9b

1 mark

(c) What is the purpose of the wooden block in this experiment?

_____

_____

9c

1 mark

(d) When the fuels are lit, they burn to release heat energy. What else is released in this reaction?

_____

9d

1 mark

(e) Some of the fuels made the bottom of the beaker turn black. What substance caused this blackness?

_____

9e

1 mark

Maximum 6 marks

10.   Max needs to pump up his football using a bicycle pump.

(a)(i) Where was the energy stored before it was transferred in pumping up the ball?

_____

10ai

1 mark

(ii)   In what form was this energy stored?

_____

10aii

1 mark

(b)(i) Max noticed that the pump became hot as he was pumping up the ball. Give one reason for this.

_____

_____

10bi

1 mark

(ii)   What effect would this increase in temperature have on the movement of the air molecules inside the ball?

_____

_____

10bii

1 mark

(iii)   What effect would an increase in temperature have on the pressure of the air inside the ball?

_____

_____

10biii

1 mark

(iv)   Explain why the presence of more air molecules inside the ball would increase the pressure in the ball.

_____

_____

_____

10biv

1 mark

Maximum 6 marks

11. A food chain from a large wood is shown below.

Lettuces ⟶ Slugs ⟶ Thrushes ⟶ Sparrow hawks

(a) In the space below, draw an appropriate pyramid of numbers for this food chain.

11a

2 marks

(b) Pesticide was used to reduce the number of caterpillars eating the lettuces. When scientists took samples they found that the sparrow hawks contained the highest concentration of insecticide. Explain the reason for this.

_____

_____

_____

11b

2 marks

(c) The pesticide was so successful at killing caterpillars that it caused the slug population to increase. What effect would this have on the sparrow hawk population, and why?

_____

_____

_____

11c

2 marks

Maximum 6 marks

12. Plant cells produce oxygen in photosynthesis. Graph X below shows how the amount of oxygen produced by a large deciduous tree varies over the course of a year.

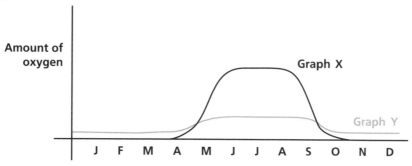

(a) Why is so much oxygen produced during the summer months?

_____

_____

(b) Which gas is taken in by the trees during the process which produces oxygen?

_____

(c) Write a word equation for this process.

_____

(d) Graph Y shows how the amount of oxygen used by the plant varies over the year. Why does this go up during the summer months?

_____

_____

(e) Deciduous trees don't keep their leaves all year round. How can you tell the tree in the graph above is deciduous?

_____

_____

Maximum 6 marks

13. (a) Look at the human characteristics listed below.

intelligence	weight	eye colour
blood group	strength	ability to speak French
attached earlobes	broken leg	speed

(i) List two characteristics that are caused purely by genetic factors.

1 _____

2 _____

13ai
1 mark

(ii) List two characteristics that are caused purely by environmental factors.

1 _____

2 _____

13aii
1 mark

(iii) List two characteristics that are caused by a combination of genetic and environmental factors.

1 _____

2 _____

13aiii
1 mark

(b) The bar chart below shows the distribution of various weights of pupils in a Year 9 class.

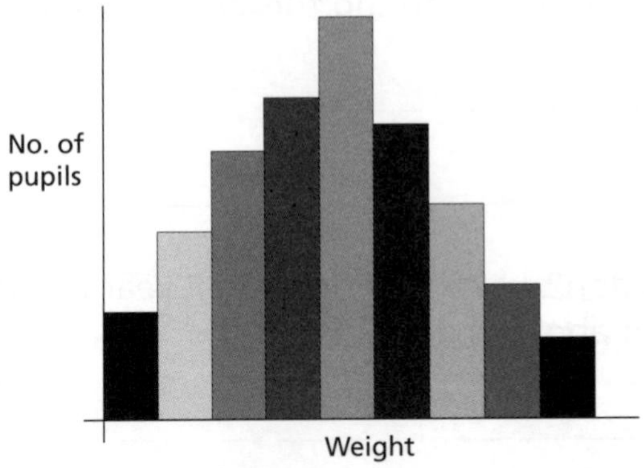

Which three features from the following list would produce a similar distribution?

Attached earlobes ☐   Eye colour ☐   Intelligence ☐

Speed ☐   Number of teeth ☐   Sex ☐

Blood group ☐   Arm span ☐

Maximum 6 marks

13b
3 marks

14. (a) John is sitting opposite his lighter sister Jill on a see-saw.

(i) If Jill moves further away from the pivot, what happens to her turning moment?

_____

14ai

1 mark

(ii) What would John need to do to keep the see-saw balanced?

_____

14aii

1 mark

(b)(i) A load of 300N is then placed 2 metres from the pivot (after the children have got off!). What is the turning moment produced by the load? (Remember to give the units.)

_____

_____

14bi

2 marks

(ii) How far from the pivot must a 100N load be placed in order to balance the 300N load?

_____

_____

14bii

1 mark

(c) Why is a tight nut more easily loosened by a long spanner than by a short spanner?

_____

_____

_____

14c

1 mark

Maximum 6 marks

15. A girl pedalling a bicycle was timed over a period of 30 secs. A graph of distance travelled against time was then drawn.

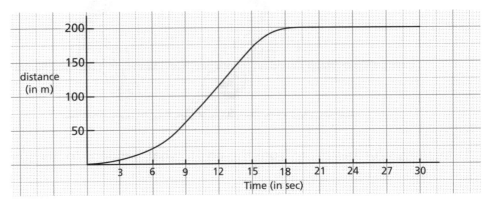

(a)(i) Describe the movement of the bicycle between 9 seconds and 15 seconds.

_____

(ii) Describe the movement of the bicycle between 15 seconds and 20 seconds.

_____

(iii) Describe the movement of the bicycle between 22 seconds and 30 seconds.

_____

(b) Calculate the average speed of the bike between 0 and 20 seconds.

_____

_____

(c) When the bicycle was travelling at a constant speed, what can you say about the frictional force compared to the forward force?

_____

Maximum 6 marks

15ai
1 mark

15aii
1 mark

15aiii
1 mark

15b
2 marks

15c
1 mark

34

Science test

Paper 1B

Please read this page carefully but do not open the booklet until you are told to start. Write your name and the name of your school in the spaces below.

First name _____

Last name _____

School name _____

Remember

- The test is 1 hour long.
- You should have the following things on your desk: pen, pencil, rubber, ruler, protractor and calculator.
- The easier questions are at the beginning of the test.
- Try your best to answer all of the questions.
- The marks available for each question are shown below the mark boxes at the side of each question.
- Do not use rough paper. Write your answers and any working on the paper itself.
- Don't forget to check your work carefully.
- Ask your teacher if you are unsure about anything.

Total marks	

For marker's
use only

Lonsdale

1.   (a)   Look at the diagram of the skin cells (epithelial cells) below.

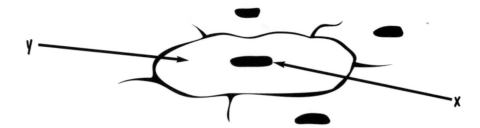

(i)   What are the black structures labelled x?

1ai

1 mark

_____

(ii)   What substance forms the 'body' of the cell, labelled y?

1aii

1 mark

_____

(iii)   Explain how skin cells (epithelial cells) are well adapted to their function.

1aiii

2 marks

_____

_____

(b)   Write down the names of the cells shown below.

_____

_____

_____

1b

2 marks

_____

Maximum 6 marks

2.

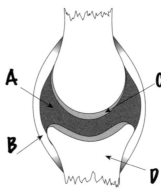

(a) The diagram above shows a knee joint. Name the structures shown in the joint.

Structure A   _____

Structure B   _____

Structure C   _____

Structure D   _____

2a

2 marks

(b)(i) What is the name given to the parts labelled X in the diagram above?

_____

2bi

1 mark

(ii) Describe one important property of this structure.

_____

2bii

1 mark

(iii) Which muscle, Y or Z, would you have to contract if you wished to lift your hand to your mouth?

_____

2biii

1 mark

(iv) Which muscle, Y or Z, would you have to contract if you did a press-up?

_____

2biv

1 mark

Maximum 6 marks

3.

Scorpion   European Leech   Roman Snail   Dor Beetle   Honey Bee

Common Earthworm   Common Mussel   Lobster   Woodlouse   Garden Spider

(a)   The diagrams above show invertebrate animals. Place them into the correct groups in the tables below. There are two animals in each group, and two have already been done for you.

Annelids		
Molluscs		Common Mussel
Crustaceans		
Arachnids		
Insects	Honey Bee	

(b)   What is an invertebrate animal?

_____

_____

(c)   Luke had jotted down some notes about the invertebrate animals he had seen in a nearby wood. Look at his descriptions below and try to identify the animal group to which they belong.

(i)   The body was divided into three parts. There were three pairs of legs and two pairs of wings. The outside was hard and shiny and it had jointed legs.
The group the animal belongs to is…

_____

(ii)   The body was divided into segments. There were bristles on the segments but no legs. I couldn't see any eyes.
The group the animal belongs to is…

_____

(iii)   The body was divided into two parts. It had four pairs of legs, which were jointed, but there were no wings. The outside of the body was hard and shiny.
The group this animal belongs to is…

_____

Maximum 6 marks

3a
2 marks

3b
1 mark

3ci
1 mark

3cii
1 mark

3ciii
1 mark

4.

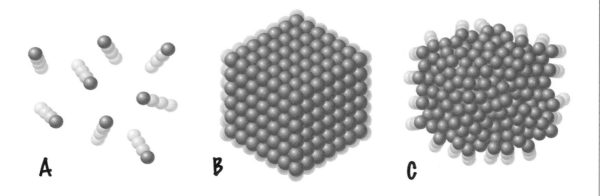

A   B   C

(a) Which one of the diagrams above would best represent a liquid?

_____

4a

1 mark

(b) Which one of the diagrams above would best represent a gas?

_____

4b

1 mark

(c) Which one of the diagrams above would best represent a solid?

_____

4c

1 mark

(d) Sarah told Rebecca that liquids have particles that:
  (i) are packed closely together
  (ii) exert no pull force between them
  (iii) move around in any direction.

Which one of these statements is wrong?

_____

4d

1 mark

(e) What happens to the particles in a liquid as the temperature of the liquid rises?

_____

_____

4e

1 mark

(f) What happens to these particles if the temperature of the liquid reaches boiling point?

_____

_____

4f

1 mark

Maximum 6 marks

5. (a) There are five common methods of separating mixtures.
- Sieving
- Filtration
- Evaporation
- Distillation
- Chromatography

Decide which of these methods would be the best way of separating the mixtures below.

Sand and gravel _____

The different pigments in paint _____

Chalk and water _____

Sugar and water _____

Alcohol and water _____

Tea leaves and tea _____

(b)

The apparatus above was used to separate two liquids. Liquid A boils at 90°C while liquid B boils at 135°C.

(i) At which point, X or Y, should the cold water enter the condenser?

_____

(ii) Which of the liquids should end up in the beaker labelled Z?

_____

(iii) What would happen if the original mixture was heated to a temperature of 135°C?

_____

_____

Maximum 6 marks

6. (a) Katie and Rachael performed a simple experiment to see what happened when a clean iron nail was placed into a beaker of copper sulphate solution. They recorded what happened by drawing the following diagrams:

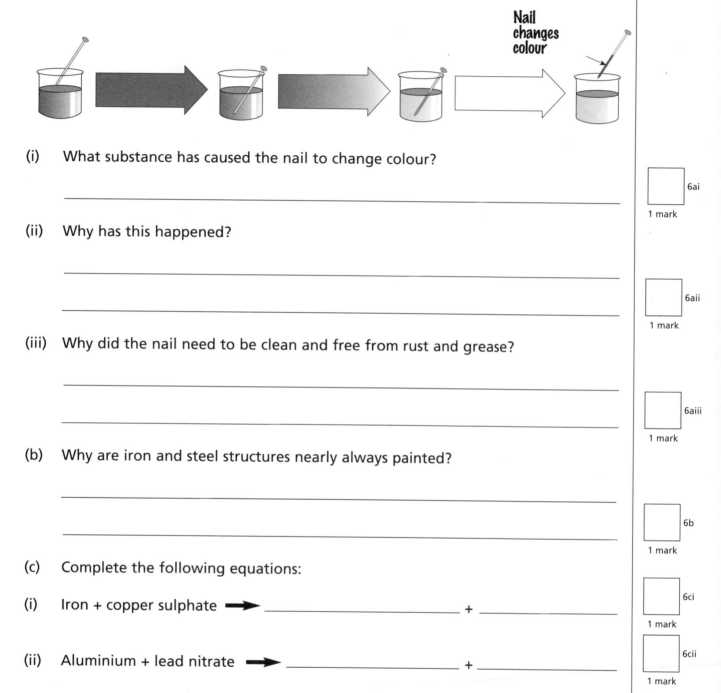

Nail changes colour

(i) What substance has caused the nail to change colour?

_____

6ai

1 mark

(ii) Why has this happened?

_____

_____

6aii

1 mark

(iii) Why did the nail need to be clean and free from rust and grease?

_____

_____

6aiii

1 mark

(b) Why are iron and steel structures nearly always painted?

_____

_____

6b

1 mark

(c) Complete the following equations:

(i) Iron + copper sulphate ➡ _____ + _____

6ci

1 mark

(ii) Aluminium + lead nitrate ➡ _____ + _____

6cii

1 mark

Maximum 6 marks

7. (a) The following electrical devices all transfer electrical energy into other forms of energy.

What is the main form of energy transfer that takes place in each device?

The electric kettle mainly transfers electrical energy into _____

The electric drill mainly transfers electrical energy into _____

The electric cooker mainly transfers electrical energy into _____

The low energy light bulb mainly transfers electrical energy into _____

7a

2 marks

(b) Which of the circuits below transfers the most energy every second? _____

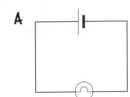 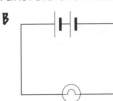

7b

1 mark

(c) On the circuit shown below, draw the position that a voltmeter would need to be placed in to measure the voltage across the lamp.

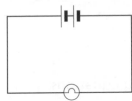

7c

1 mark

(d) For each of the following circuits, write down the value of the missing voltage.

(i)

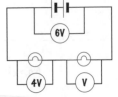

V = _____ volts

7di

1 mark

(ii)

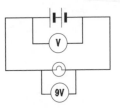

V = _____ volts

7dii

1 mark

Maximum 6 marks

8. (a) Name a unit of pressure.

_____

8a

1 mark

(b) Why are high-heeled shoes banned from certain types of floor?

_____

_____

8b

1 mark

(c) Write down the formula for pressure.

_____

_____

8c

1 mark

(d) With specific reference to pressure, why is it an advantage for camels to have big feet?

_____

_____

8d

1 mark

(e) Calculate the pressure exerted on the ground by each hoof if a horse has a weight of 5 000N and each hoof has an area of 125cm².

_____

_____

_____

_____

8e

2 marks

Maximum 6 marks

9.

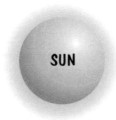

SUN

EARTH

URANUS

(a) Uranus can be seen from Earth. Explain how this is possible.

_____

_____

9a

1 mark

(b) If there was life on Uranus, explain why the amount of biomass on Uranus would be likely to be far less than that on Earth. (Biomass is the mass of living material.)

_____

_____

9b

1 mark

(c) Name one planet that is between Earth and Uranus.

_____

9c

1 mark

(d) Use the words and phrases below to fill in the table comparing Earth with Uranus.

Colder   **Takes a longer time to orbit the sun**   **Receives less light**

Receives more light   **Warmer**   **Takes a shorter time to orbit the sun**

Earth	Uranus

9d

3 marks

Maximum 6 marks

10. (a) The diagram below shows the various stages leading to the production of an embryo.

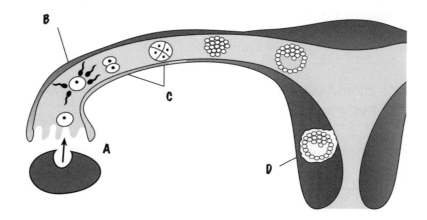

Use the words below to name the parts of the diagram which are indicated.

Implantation　　　**Fertilisation**　　　**Ovulation**　　　**Cell Division**

A _____

B _____

C _____

D _____

10a	2 marks

(b) What is the name given to the structure which attaches the baby to the uterus?

_____

10b	1 mark

(c) Name two substances which pass from the mother's blood into the baby's blood.

1 _____

2 _____

10c	1 mark

(d) Name two substances which pass from the baby's blood into the mother's blood.

1 _____

2 _____

10d	1 mark

(e) What is the purpose of the amniotic fluid which surrounds the baby in the uterus?

_____

10e	1 mark

Maximum 6 marks

11.   Karen and David own a racehorse. They think that it would be a good idea to mate her with a top-class male racehorse to produce a foal which will turn out to be an even better racehorse.

(a)   Does Karen and David's plan have a good chance of working? Explain your answer.

_____

_____

_____

11a
1 mark

(b)   Use the words from the list below to complete the following sentences.

characteristic   varieties   variation   offspring

New _____ of organism can be bred by taking advantage of

_____ . Organisms with a desired _____ are bred with

similar organisms resulting in _____ , some of which will have an

exaggerated version of this characteristic.

11b
2 marks

(c)(i) Plot the data below onto the graph paper provided.

Year	Average animal milk yield (litres per year)
1900	1 500
1920	1 700
1940	2 300
1960	3 200
1980	3 900
2000	4 400

11ci
2 marks

(ii)   The rate of increase in the milk yield appears to be slowing down. Give a reason for this.

_____

_____

11cii
1 mark

Maximum 6 marks

12. Duncan and Matthew performed an experiment on a waxy substance which melts at 50°C. They bored a hole in the waxy substance at room temperature and inserted a thermometer.

They gently heated the waxy substance with a Bunsen burner. The temperature of the substance rose in the way shown in the graph.

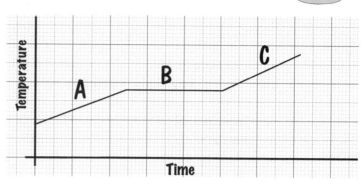

(a) Explain what is happening during stage A.

_____

_____

12a
1 mark

(b) Explain what is happening during stage B.

_____

_____

12b
1 mark

(c) Explain what is happening during stage C.

_____

_____

12c
1 mark

(d) On the graph paper below, draw a graph to represent what would happen if the waxy substance was allowed to cool down.

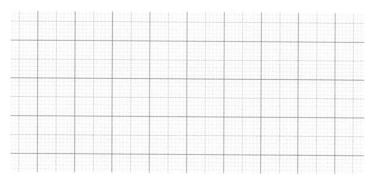

(e) If Duncan and Matthew had continued to heat the waxy substance, the temperature would have continued to rise. What eventually would have happened to the waxy substance?

_____

12d
2 marks

12e
1 mark

Maximum 6 marks

13. (a) The table below gives the names of three different rocks, and the rock types to which they belong.

Name of rock	Basalt	Slate	Limestone
Rock type	Igneous	Metamorphic	Sedimentary

In the diagram below, draw lines to show how each rock was formed and to identify the key features of the rock.

Key features of the rock	Name of rock	Details of rock formation
Small crystals in layers or bands	Basalt	Formed from layers of shell particles becoming cemented together
Small crystals formed by fast cooling	Slate	Formed by the quick cooling of magma expelled from volcanoes
Grainy and crumbly, may contain fossils	Limestone	Formed by the effect of heat and pressure on mudstone

13a

3 marks

(b) The picture below shows weathering of a limestone statue.

(i) Explain how chemical weathering of limestone happens.

_____

_____

_____

13bi

2 marks

(ii) If water enters cracks in any rock type, physical weathering can take place. Explain what is meant by physical weathering.

_____

_____

13bii

1 mark

Maximum 6 marks

14. (a) Grace was investigating the way current flowed through simple circuits. She set up the following circuit:

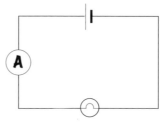

Grace noted the ammeter reading. It was 0.4 amps.

(i) What would the ammeter reading be if Grace added another identical bulb alongside the first bulb?

_____

14ai

1 mark

(ii) What would the ammeter reading be if Grace changed her circuit back to one bulb but added another identical cell alongside the first cell?

_____

14aii

1 mark

(b) Grace then changed her circuit so that it looked like this:

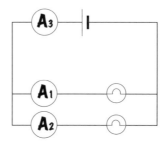

(i) What would Grace expect to find when she examined ammeters A1 and A2?

_____

14bi

1 mark

(ii) If ammeter A2 showed a reading of 0.2 amps, what would the expected readings be on:

A1 _____

A3 _____

14bii

2 marks

(c) What kind of circuit had Grace constructed in part (b) using two bulbs?

_____

14c

1 mark

Maximum 6 marks

15. Ian and Richard made an electromagnet by winding copper wire around a cardboard toilet roll core as shown in the diagram below.

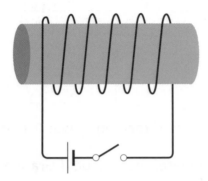

They decided to investigate the strength of the electromagnet by seeing how many paper clips it could pick up, and how increasing the number of coils on the magnet would affect this.

(a) Name two things that would need to be kept the same in order to make this a fair test.

1 _____

2 _____

15a

2 marks

(b) Describe three ways in which the magnet could be made more powerful.

1 _____

2 _____

15b

3 _____

3 marks

(c) What happens to the magnetic field formed by this magnet when the switch is opened?

_____

15c

_____

1 mark

Maximum 6 marks

Sc

KEY STAGE
3

TIER
5- 7

Science test

Paper 2B

Please read this page carefully but do not open the booklet until you are told to start. Write your name and the name of your school in the spaces below.

First name ______________________

Last name ______________________

School name ______________________

Remember

- The test is 1 hour long.
- You should have the following things on your desk: pen, pencil, rubber, ruler, protractor and calculator.
- The easier questions are at the beginning of the test.
- Try your best to answer all of the questions.
- The marks available for each question are shown below the mark boxes at the side of each question.
- Do not use rough paper. Write your answers and any working on the paper itself.
- Don't forget to check your work carefully.
- Ask your teacher if you are unsure about anything.

Total marks	

For marker's use only

Lonsdale

1.   The diagram below shows a plant cell.

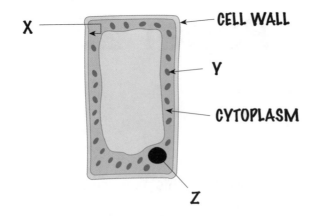

(a)   Name the parts that are labelled X, Y and Z on the diagram.

(i)   X _____

(ii)   Y _____

(iii) Z _____

(b)   Which part of the plant cell controls what enters and leaves the cell?

_____

(c)   Which part of the plant cell contains the genetic material?

_____

(d)   In which part of the plant cell does photosynthesis take place?

_____

Maximum 6 marks

2. Amy and Jacques planted some cress seeds in four different trays so that each tray of seeds had different growing conditions.

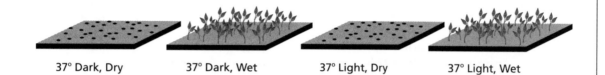

37° Dark, Dry   37° Dark, Wet   37° Light, Dry   37° Light, Wet

(a) Which factor would seem to be necessary for the germination of the seeds?

_____

2a
1 mark

(b) Which factor is it impossible to comment on?

_____

2b
1 mark

(c) How could you perform a fair investigation to discover whether this factor has any effect?

_____

_____

_____

_____

_____

2c
4 marks

Maximum 6 marks

3.   In an investigation into how the digestive system works, a visking tubing 'bag' was filled with a mixture of starch solution and sugar solution, and then sealed.

The bag was then placed in a boiling tube containing pure water and was allowed to stand for one hour. After this time had passed, a sample was taken from the water in the boiling tube and tested for both sugar and starch solutions.

(a)   What test would be used to test for starch solution?

_____

3a
1 mark

(b)   What test would be used to test for sugar solution?

_____

3b
1 mark

(c)(i)   What would you expect to find in the water of the boiling tube after one hour?

_____

3ci
1 mark

(ii)   Explain your answer to part (i)

_____

_____

3cii
2 marks

(d)   Starch is converted to sugar in the human digestive system. What is the name of the substance which causes this?

_____

3d
1 mark

Maximum 6 marks

Lonsdale

4.   (a)   Draw lines from the two central boxes below to mach up metal elements and non-metal elements to their characteristics. Draw four lines only.

Not shiny, half are gases		Metal elements		Shiny solid at room temperature
Good conductors of heat and electricity		Non metal elements		Poor conductors of heat and electricity

4a
4 marks

   (b)   Look at the following list. Underline two substances which are elements.

   carbon   water   brass   ice   oxygen   carbon dioxide   plastic

4b
1 mark

   (c)   Look at the following list. Underline two substances which are metal elements.

   sulphur   helium   tin   nitrogen   calcium   chlorine   hydrogen

4c
1 mark

Maximum 6 marks

5. In an experiment to compare the amount of energy in different foods, the following apparatus was used.

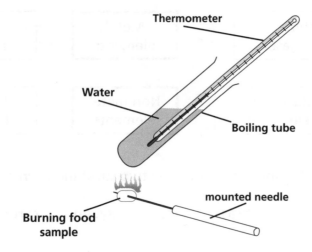

(a) In order to make a fair comparison between the energy in a peanut and the energy in a piece of bread, which three variables would need to be controlled?

1 _____

2 _____

3 _____

5a

3 marks

(b) What would have to be measured in order to make the comparison?

_____

5b

1 mark

(c) Why would this apparatus provide only a rough comparison between the two food types?

_____

5c

1 mark

(d) In this investigation, peanuts were found to contain more energy than bread. Explain the reason for this.

_____

_____

5d

1 mark

Maximum 6 marks

6. The eight metals below have been placed in order of their reactivity.

potassium   sodium   calcium   magnesium   aluminium   zinc   iron   copper

most reactive ⟵─────────────────────────────⟶ least reactive

(a) Predict what will happen when the following occur:

(i) A piece of iron is placed in copper sulphate solution.

_____

_____

| 6ai |
| 1 mark |

(ii) A piece of copper is placed in magnesium nitrate solution.

_____

_____

| 6aii |
| 1 mark |

(iii) A mixture of aluminium powder and iron oxide is heated.

_____

_____

| 6aiii |
| 1 mark |

(iv) A piece of magnesium is placed in aluminium sulphate solution.

_____

_____

| 6aiv |
| 1 mark |

(b) Gold is lower than copper in the reactivity series. Explain why gold is found in pure form.

_____

| 6b |
| 1 mark |

(c) When a piece of sodium is dropped into water it produces hydrogen quickly as it whizzes about, and it also gets very hot. Predict what would happen if potassium was placed in water.

_____

| 6c |
| 1 mark |

Maximum 6 marks

7. (a) Sonia and Elaine set up the circuit below and experimented with the switches to see the effect on the lamps.

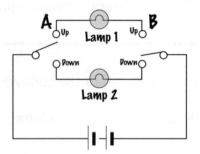

Complete the table below to show their findings.

SWITCH A	SWITCH B	LAMP 1 (ON or OFF)	LAMP 2 (ON or OFF)
UP	DOWN		
UP	UP		
DOWN	UP		
DOWN	DOWN		

7a

4 marks

(b) Sonia and Elaine then set up the circuits below.

(i)

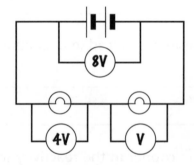

What reading would you expect to see on the voltmeter V?

_____

7bi

1 mark

(ii)

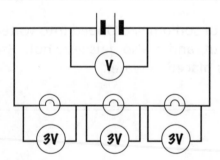

What reading would you expect to see on the voltmeter V?

7bii

1 mark

_____

Maximum 6 marks

Lonsdale

8.   (a)   Amir went on a cycling holiday. The holiday lasted for 4 days. Complete the table below showing his daily progress.

Day	Distance travelled (km)	Time taken (hours)	Average speed
1	60	5	
2		6	15
3	70		14
4		7	16

8a

4 marks

(b)   What unit is his average speed measured in?

_____

8b

1 mark

(c)   When Amir applies his brakes, what force slows the bike down?

_____

8c

1 mark

Maximum 6 marks

9.   Two pupils were investigating how the size of a shadow varies as the object making the shadow, or the light source, or the screen the shadow is created on, is moved.

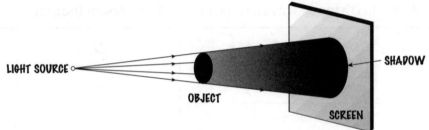

(a)   What happens to the size of the shadow if the screen is moved away from the object?

_____

9a

1 mark

(b)   What happens to the size of the shadow if the light source is moved further away from the object?

_____

9b

1 mark

(c)   What happens to the size of the shadow if the object is moved closer to the light source?

_____

9c

1 mark

(d)   Complete the ray of light shown in the diagram below.

← Mirror

A

9d

1 mark

(e)   What is the name of angle A?

_____

9e

1 mark

(f)   In reflection at a plane surface, what is angle A always equal to?

_____

9f

1 mark

Maximum 6 marks

10. Tom and Jerry were investigating the effect of temperature on enzyme activity by measuring the time it took for the enzyme amylase to completely break down starch to sugar. Every 30 seconds, they removed a drop from the beaker and tested it for starch, using iodine. They repeated this at different temperatures.

Tom's results

Temperature	Time taken to break down starch to sugar
0°C	No result
10°C	300 seconds
20°C	180 seconds
30°C	120 seconds
40°C	60 seconds
50°C	180 seconds

Jerry's results

Temperature	Time taken to break down starch to sugar
0°C	No result
10°C	330 seconds
20°C	210 seconds
30°C	90 seconds
40°C	90 seconds
50°C	150 seconds

(a) Plot these results onto the graph paper provided, making sure that you label the axes.

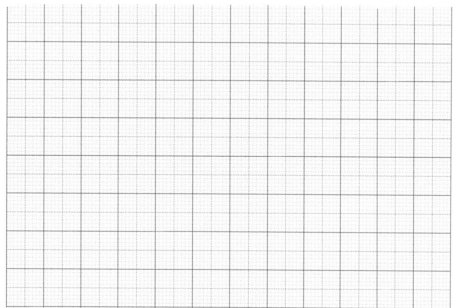

10a

4 marks

(b) Name one variable which would need to be controlled in order to make this a fair test.

_____

10b

1 mark

(c) Why was there no result at 0°C?

_____

_____

Maximum 6 marks

10c

1 mark

11. A special piece of equipment can be safely used by humans to measure the amount of carbon dioxide they breathe out and the temperature of the exhaled air. In this investigation, the equipment was fitted to a 13-year-old boy who sat and watched television while readings were taken over a period of one hour. The equipment was then fitted to a 22-year-old woman who ran steadily on a treadmill for one hour while readings were taken. The results showed that the temperature of the air breathed out by the woman was nearly 2°C higher than that breathed out by the boy, and that she produced twice as much carbon dioxide.

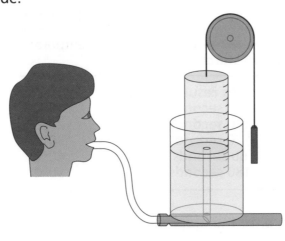

(a) Why was the temperature of the woman's exhaled air higher than the boy's?

_____

_____

11a   1 mark

(b) Give two reasons why the woman breathed out far more carbon dioxide than the boy.

_____

_____

11b   2 marks

(c) What two conclusions could you draw from this experiment about the product of respiration?

_____

_____

11c   2 marks

(d) State one way in which you would change this investigation in order to make it a fairer, more meaningful comparison.

_____

_____

11d   1 mark

Maximum 6 marks

12.   The following rocks are common throughout the British Isles.

limestone   basalt   slate   granite   sandstone   marble

(a)   Which one of the rocks above is formed from the shells of dead sea creatures?

_____

12a

1 mark

(b)   Which one of the rocks is a sedimentary rock which is not formed from the shells of dead sea creatures?

_____

12b

1 mark

(c)(i) Which one of the rocks is formed as a result of heat and pressure on limestone?

_____

12ci

1 mark

(ii)   What is the name given to the type of rock that is formed in this way?

_____

12cii

1 mark

(d)   Which two of the rocks are igneous rocks?

1   _____

2   _____

12d

2 marks

Maximum 6 marks

13. In an investigation into the effect of acid rain on carbonate rocks, some pupils added pieces of limestone to acids of different pH. They weighed the rocks before they started and then weighed them every day until they had dissolved to exactly half of their original mass. They recorded their results and these are shown below.

pH	Time taken to dissolve
6	19 days
2	7 days
4	12 days
5	16 days
3	9 days
1	2 days

(a) Plot these results on the graph paper below.

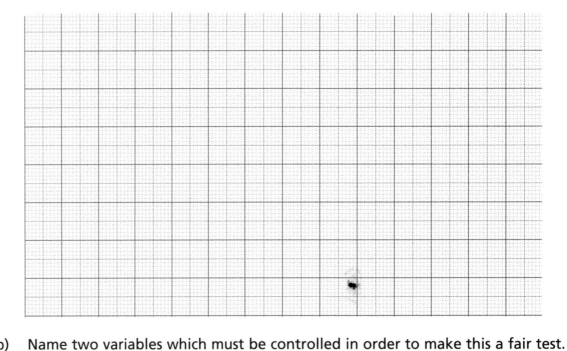

13a

3 marks

(b) Name two variables which must be controlled in order to make this a fair test.

1 _____

13b

2 _____

2 marks

(c) Which gas is given off in the reaction between limestone and dilute hydrochloric acid?

13c

_____

1 mark

Maximum 6 marks

14. The table below gives the stopping distance on a dry road surface for a vehicle travelling at various speeds.

Speed (m.p.h)	10	20	30	40	50	60
Stopping distance (m)	5	15	32	49	71	105

(a)(i) What effect does speed have on stopping distance?

_____

14ai

1 mark

(ii) What force acts to slow down the vehicle when the brakes are applied?

_____

14aii

1 mark

(b) Name three factors which could increase these stopping distances.

1 _____

2 _____

3 _____

14b

3 marks

(c) Wider tyres were then put onto the vehicle. What effect would this have on the stopping distance?

_____

14c

1 mark

Maximum 6 marks

15. You have been asked to investigate how the insulating properties of a material depends on its thickness. Foam is wrapped around a can containing hot water. The temperature of the water is measured every 5 minutes for 20 minutes. The experiment is then repeated with foam of a different thickness.

(a) Give three variables that you need to control in order to make this a fair test.

1 _____

2 _____

3 _____

(b) By what method would most of the heat be transferred to the surroundings?

_____

(c) What effect would placing the can in a vacuum have on the rate of cooling? Explain your answer.

_____

_____

Maximum 6 marks

15a
3 marks

15b
1 mark

15c
2 marks

Sc

KEY STAGE
3

TIER
5- 7

Science test

Paper 1C

Please read this page carefully but do not open the booklet until you are told to start. Write your name and the name of your school in the spaces below.

First name ______________________________

Last name ______________________________

School name ______________________________

Remember

- The test is 1 hour long.
- You should have the following things on your desk: pen, pencil, rubber, ruler, protractor and calculator.
- The easier questions are at the beginning of the test.
- Try your best to answer all of the questions.
- The marks available for each question are shown below the mark boxes at the side of each question.
- Do not use rough paper. Write your answers and any working on the paper itself.
- Don't forget to check your work carefully.
- Ask your teacher if you are unsure about anything.

Total marks	

For marker's use only

Lonsdale

1. (a) Look at the following set of data.

NUMBER OF CIGARETTES SMOKED PER DAY	10	20	30	40	50
INCREASED RISK OF DYING OF LUNG CANCER	x10	x18	x25	x33	x40

What can you say about how smoking can affect your chances of dying of lung cancer?

_____

_____

(b) Now look at this set of data.

YEAR	1920	1930	1940	1950	1960
NUMBER OF DEATHS PER 100,000 DUE TO LUNG CANCER	10	35	50	100	180

What conclusion can you draw from this data?

_____

_____

(c) Read the following sentences about smoking and fill in the blanks using the words below.

nicotine   **carbon monoxide**   **air sacs (alveoli)**   **cilia**

Heart rate and blood pressure are increased by _____ which is an addictive substance in cigarette smoke.

Constant coughing due to a build up of mucus damages the _____ . This can result in an illness called emphysema.

The tar causes mucus to build up and this stops the _____ from 'beating'.

_____ from smoke prevents oxygen from being absorbed by the blood since it combines more easily with the blood.

Maximum 6 marks

2. The diagram below shows the digestive system.

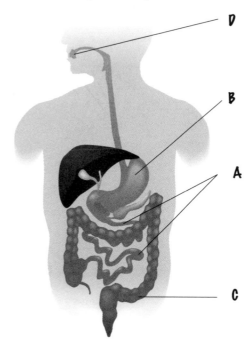

(a) What is the name given to part A ?

_____

2a

1 mark

(b) What is the name given to part B?

_____

2b

1 mark

(c) What is the name given to part C?

_____

2c

1 mark

(d) What is the name given to part D?

_____

2d

1 mark

After a meal the food you have eaten passes slowly through the digestive system where various things happen to it.

(e) In which part of the digestive system are all the nutrients from the food absorbed into the bloodstream?

_____

2e

1 mark

(f) In which part of the digestive system is water reabsorbed into the body?

_____

2f

1 mark

Maximum 6 marks

3.   Yasmin investigated the organisms which lived in her local wood and produced the following simple food web.

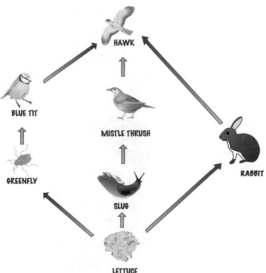

(a)   Write down an example of a food chain from this food web in the spaces below.

_____ ➤ _____ ➤ _____ ➤ _____

3a
1 mark

(b)   Write down the name of one carnivore from the food web.

_____

3b
1 mark

(c)   Write down the name of two herbivores from the food web.

_____

3c
2 marks

(d)   Explain what would happen to the number of thrushes eaten by hawks if the blue tits died out.

_____

3d
1 mark

(e)   What is the original source of energy for all the seven organisms in the food web?

_____

3e
1 mark

Maximum 6 marks

4. Grace and James performed an experiment to see how easily salt dissolved in water. They used water at different temperatures which was placed into glass beakers. The salt was added using a small spoon and was stirred until it dissolved. The number of spoonfuls dissolved in each beaker was noted.

Temperature of water (°C)	Number of spoonfuls of salt which dissolved
10	3
20	5
30	9

(a) What conclusion can be drawn by Grace and James about how the solubility of salt changes as the temperature of the water increases?

_____

_____

4a

1 mark

(b) What else, apart from the amount of stirring, would need to be kept the same in order for this to be a fair test?

_____

_____

4b

1 mark

(c) Grace and James then experimented with three other types of solvent. The ones they chose were alcohol, petrol and turpentine. Name two things which they would have to keep the same in order for this to be a fair test.

_____

_____

4c

2 marks

(d) What factor would you expect Grace and James to measure in this second investigation? And what units should they use?

_____

_____

4d

2 marks

Maximum 6 marks

5.   Some Year 9 pupils used the equipment below to investigate how increasing the amount of metal in a chemical reaction with acid affected the amount of gas given off. They continued to add acid until all the metal had disappeared. Their results are shown below.

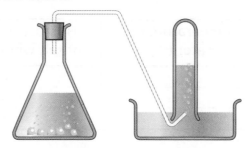

Mass of metal (g)	0.5	1.0	1.5	2.0	2.5	3.0	3.5	4.0
Volume of gas (cm³)	400	900	1300	1800	2000	2700	3200	3700

(a)   Suggest one thing you might observe which would tell you that the acid and the metal were taking part in a chemical reaction.

5a

1 mark

(b)   If the acid was hydrochloric and the metal was zinc, which gas would be formed?

5b

1 mark

(c)   Plot the results onto the graph paper below ensuring that the points are plotted accurately. Draw a line of best fit.

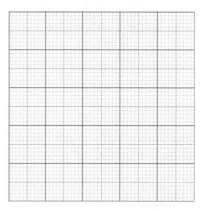

5c

2 marks

(d)   What conclusion can you draw from these results?

5d

1 mark

(e)   What can you say about the accuracy of these results?

5e

1 mark

Maximum 6 marks

6. (a) Put a circle around the elements in this list.

    Oxygen   Salt   Iron   Wood   Water   Sodium   Carbon dioxide   Gold

    6a
    1 mark

    (b) Write down the names of two gases from the list above.

    1 _____

    2 _____

    6b
    1 mark

    (c) Write down the names of two metals from the list above.

    1 _____

    2 _____

    6c
    1 mark

    (d) Write down the name of a compound which contains only hydrogen and oxygen.

    _____

    6d
    1 mark

    Look at the following list of substances.

    Magnesium   Sulphur   Helium   Sodium chloride   Oxygen

    (e) Write down the name of a substance from this list, which is a shiny solid at room temperature and is also a good conductor of heat and electricity.

    _____

    6e
    1 mark

    (f) Write down the name of an inert gas from this list, which is lighter than air.

    _____

    6f
    1 mark

    Maximum 6 marks

7. (a) An aeroplane travelling from London to Rome covers 200km in 15min.

    (i) What was the average speed of the aeroplane? Please include the unit.

_____

_____

7ai

1 mark

    (ii) What can you say about how the forward force on the aeroplane compares with the backward force when it is travelling at a constant speed?

_____

_____

7aii

1 mark

    (b) Halfway through the journey the pilot experiences engine problems and has to reduce the amount of thrust produced by them.

    (i) As he reduces the thrust how does the forward force now compare with the backward force?

_____

_____

7bi

1 mark

    (ii) What immediate effect will this have on the speed of the aeroplane?

_____

7bii

1 mark

    (c) The pilot finds that he can't solve the problem and must continue in this way for the rest of the trip.

    (i) Assuming the thrust stays at the same reduced level and external conditions remain the same, what can you say about the new speed of the aeroplane in addition to what you have said in answer to the previous question?

_____

_____

7ci

1 mark

    (ii) How can you explain this in terms of the forward and backward forces on the aeroplane?

_____

7cii

1 mark

Maximum 6 marks

8. A group of students is investigating how the strength of an electromagnet depends on the number of coils of wire it consists of. They are going to count the number of paper clips the different sized electromagnets can pick up.

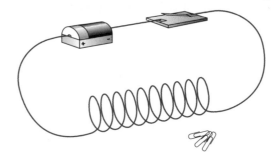

(a) Name one factor which must be kept the same in order to make this a fair test.

8a

1 mark

(b) The students' results are shown below. They carried out each experiment three times for each electromagnet. Complete the table by working out the average results.

Coils of wire	No. of paperclips picked up			
	Expt 1	Expt 2	Expt 3	Average
5	4	4	4	
10	9	8	7	
15	13	12	11	
20	18	16	17	
25	21	20	22	
30	24	23	25	

8b

2 marks

(c) Plot these results on the graph paper below and draw a line of best fit.

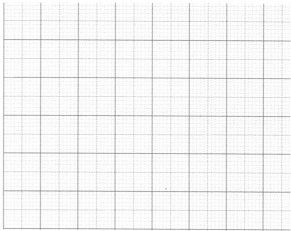

8c

2 marks

(d) What conclusion can the group draw from these results?

8d

1 mark

Maximum 6 marks

9. If there is a difference in temperature between any object and its surroundings then this difference results in a flow of energy from the hotter region to the cooler region, i.e. the object can either take in heat energy or give out heat energy depending on whether it is hotter or cooler than its surroundings.

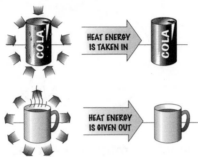

(a) What are the four ways in which heat energy can be transferred from one place to another?

1 _____

2 _____

3 _____

4 _____

9a

2 marks

(b) Identify the main way in which heat energy is transferred in each of the following examples.

(i) Heat energy travelling along an iron bar, one end of which has been placed in a furnace.

_____

9bi

1 mark

(ii) Heat energy from the sun reaching the earth.

_____

9bii

1 mark

(iii) Heat energy from an immersion heater spreading throughout a tank of water.

_____

9biii

1 mark

(c) Besides heat energy, what else is lost from a bowl of water as it evaporates?

_____

9c

1 mark

Maximum 6 marks

10. During photosynthesis plants take in carbon dioxide from the atmosphere, water from the soil and light energy from the sun.

(a) Which two substances are produced during photosynthesis?

1_____

2_____

10a

1 mark

(b) What storage carbohydrate does the plant produce from one of the above?

_____

10b

1 mark

(c) What is this storage carbohydrate broken down to in the digestive system of animals which eat these plants?

_____

10c

1 mark

(d) This carbohydrate is then respired inside living cells. Write down a word equation for respiration.

_____

_____

10d

1 mark

(e) Give one example of how energy from respiration is 'used' in living organisms.

_____

10e

1 mark

(f) Which organisms then absorb the gas produced in respiration?

_____

10f

1 mark

Maximum 6 marks

11. Tippi and Will investigated how the presence of chlorophyll affected the amount of starch produced in leaves. They used variegated leaves in which only the green parts of the leaves contain chlorophyll.

Firstly they removed a leaf and placed it in boiling water for 30 seconds. Then they dabbed it dry and placed it into hot alcohol for 3-4 minutes. The alcohol was heated by a water bath. After this they placed it back into hot water for a further minute or so, before once again blotting away excess water. The leaf was then placed onto a white tile and covered in iodine solution. After 3-4 minutes the excess iodine was blotted away.

(a) Why was the leaf placed in boiling water at the beginning of the experiment?

_____

11a

1 mark

(b) Why was the leaf placed into alcohol?

_____

11b

1 mark

(c) Why was the alcohol heated by a water bath?

_____

11c

1 mark

(d) What colour was the iodine solution originally?

_____

11d

1 mark

(e) What difference in colour would you expect between the green parts of the leaf and the pale parts of the leaf after iodine had been added?

_____

_____

11e

1 mark

(f) What conclusion can be drawn from this?

_____

_____

11f

1 mark

Maximum 6 marks

12. (a) Complete the following word equations for the reactions of metals with oxygen. If there is no reaction, write 'no reaction'.

Iron + oxygen ⟶ _____

Magnesium + oxygen ⟶ _____

Copper + oxygen ⟶ _____

Sodium + oxygen ⟶ _____

12a
2 marks

(b) Complete the following word equations for the reactions of metals with water. If there is no reaction, write 'no reaction'.

Calcium + water ⟶ _____

Copper + water ⟶ _____

Potassium + water ⟶ _____

Gold + water ⟶ _____

12b
2 marks

(c) The diagram below shows pieces of metal reacting with acid in beakers.

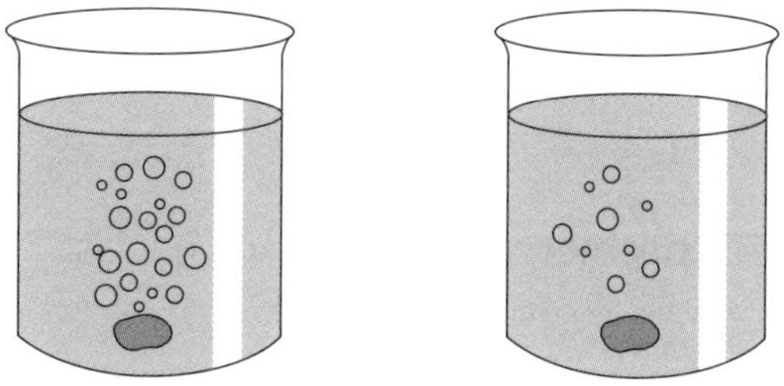

Besides a gas, what else is produced during a reaction between a metal and an acid?

_____

12c
1 mark

(d) Complete the following word equations for the reactions of metals with acids. If there is no reaction write 'no reaction'.

Zinc + hydrochloric acid ⟶ _____

Iron + sulphuric acid ⟶ _____

12d
1 mark

Maximum 6 marks

13. Some houses in the Yorkshire Dales and Derbyshire are made from limestone in which fossils are often found.

(a) Why can fossils be found in limestone?

_____

_____

(b) Houses made from limestone often show signs of quite severe weathering. Explain why you would expect this.

_____

_____

(c) Why has this problem got worse in the last 100 years?

_____

_____

(d) Name a gas which has contributed to this problem.

_____

(e) Write down the word equation for the reaction of limestone with dilute hydrochloric acid.

_____

_____

(f) How would you know a chemical reaction like the one above was taking place?

_____

Maximum 6 marks

14. (a) The following statements are all about sound, such as that made by plucking a guitar string. Tick the ones that are correct.

   (i)   We hear sounds because our ear drum vibrates. ☐

   (ii) All sounds are caused by vibrations. ☐

   (iii) Sound travels faster than light. ☐

   (iv) Sound is not a form of energy. ☐

   14a

   2 marks

(b) The diagrams below show the traces of four different sounds on an oscilloscope.

A 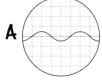   B   C 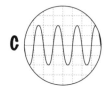   D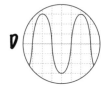

   (i) Which trace shows the biggest amplitude?

   _____

   14bi

   1 mark

   (ii) Which trace shows the quietest sound?

   _____

   14bii

   1 mark

   (iii) Which trace shows the highest pitch?

   _____

   14biii

   1 mark

   (iv) Which two diagrams show different pitch but the same loudness?

   _____

   14biv

   1 mark

Maximum 6 marks

15. Gail is carrying out an investigation into the principle of moments. She has a 1 metre ruler of uniform thickness which is pivoted at the 50cm mark - the centre of the ruler. She then suspends weights on each side of the pivot and alters their position until the ruler is balanced.

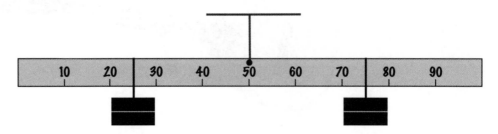

(a) Complete the tables below which show the results she got.

Clockwise		
Weight (N)	Distance (cm)	Moment (Ncm)
1	20	
2	20	
3	20	
4	20	

Anti-clockwise		
Weight (N)	Distance (cm)	Moment (Ncm)
2	9	
2	21	
2	30	
2	39	

15a
2 marks

(b) Draw a straight line graph to show her results.

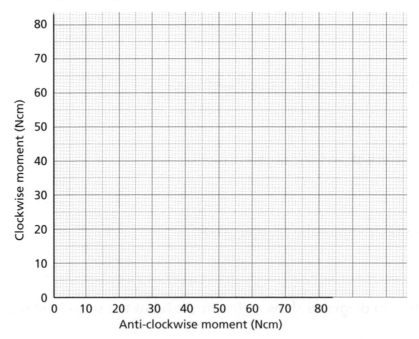

15b
3 marks

(c) What conclusion can Gail reach looking at her results?

_____

_____

15c
1 mark

Maximum 6 marks

Science test

Paper 2C

Please read this page carefully but do not open the booklet until you are told to start. Write your name and the name of your school in the spaces below.

First name _____

Last name _____

School name _____

Remember

- The test is 1 hour long.
- You should have the following things on your desk: pen, pencil, rubber, ruler, protractor and calculator.
- The easier questions are at the beginning of the test.
- Try your best to answer all of the questions.
- The marks available for each question are shown below the mark boxes at the side of each question.
- Do not use rough paper. Write your answers and any working on the paper itself.
- Don't forget to check your work carefully.
- Ask your teacher if you are unsure about anything.

Total marks	

For marker's
use only

Lonsdale

1.

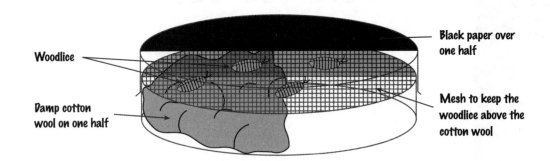

Woodlice

Black paper over one half

Damp cotton wool on one half

Mesh to keep the woodlice above the cotton wool

(a) Name two factors that must be kept the same in order to make this a fair test.

1 _____

2 _____

(b) The students obtained the following results by recording where the woodlice were every 2 minutes.

TIME	0	2	4	6	8	10
Wet and dark	5	11	16	18	19	20
Wet and light	5	3	1	0	0	0
Dry and dark	5	4	3	2	1	0
Dry and light	5	2	0	0	0	0

(i) What conclusion can you draw from this investigation about where woodlice like to live?

_____

(ii) How many woodlice were used in this investigation?

_____

(iii) What sort of conditions do woodlice like least?

_____

(c) If this investigation had used only 4 woodlice, would the results have been as useful? Explain you answer.

_____

Maximum 6 marks

1a

2 marks

1bi

1 mark

1bii

1 mark

1biii

1 mark

1c

1 mark

2. (a) Complete the following passage by filling in the blanks.

Organisms of different species can be placed into groups based on their

observable _____ . Animals with backbones are called

_____ , while those without backbones are called

_____ . Animals with backbones can be further subdivided

into mammals, birds, _____ , _____ and fish.

Only _____ have hair and suckle their young.

2a

3 marks

(b)(i) Which animal group has a body divided into three parts, three pairs of legs, wings, an external skeleton and jointed legs?

_____

2bi

1 mark

(ii) Which animal group can breathe through moist skin and needs water in order to breed?

_____

2bii

1 mark

(iii) Which animal group has a body which is divided into segments, each one of which has bristles?

_____

2biii

1 mark

Maximum 6 marks

3. A person's heart rate and breathing rate (ventilation rate) were monitored while they were in a resting position and then as they gradually increased the speed at which they were running. The following results were obtained.

Activity	Heart rate (beats per minute)	Ventilation rate (breaths per minute)
At rest	60	9
Walking	70	13
Slow jog	90	17
Steady jog	100	23
Fast jog	120	25
Nearly flat out	140	30
Flat out sprint	160	31

(a) Draw a line graph of these results on the graph paper below.

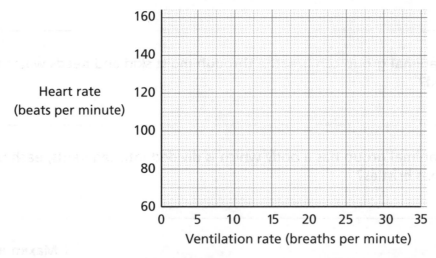

(b) Describe the link between heart rate and ventilation rate.

_____

_____

(c)(i) The heart and lungs form the cardiovascular system.
Name two things they supply to the working muscle tissue.

1 _____

2 _____

(ii) Name two things they remove from the working muscle tissue.

1 _____

2 _____

Maximum 6 marks

3a
1 mark

3b
1 mark

3ci
2 marks

3cii
2 marks

4.   The table below gives data for the melting points and boiling points of 12 different elements.

Symbol of element	Na	Al	O	Ca	Hg	Au	He	Pb	S	Cu	Ni	K
Melting point °C	98	660	-219	840	-39	1064	-270	328	119	1083	1455	63
Boiling point °C	900	2400	-183	1490	357	2850	-269	1750	445	2580	2150	770

(a)(i) Which element(s) are solid at a room temperature of 20°C?

_____

4ai

1 mark

(ii)   Which element(s) are liquid at a room temperature of 20°C?

_____

4aii

1 mark

(iii)   Which element(s) are a gas at a room temperature of 20°C?

_____

4aiii

1 mark

(b)(i) Which element has the biggest difference between its melting point and boiling point?

_____

4bi

1 mark

(ii)   Which element has the smallest difference between its melting point and boiling point?

_____

4bii

1 mark

(c)   Which element is a non-metallic solid at room temperature?

_____

4c

1 mark

Maximum 6 marks

5.   Some pupils performed an investigation into how salt affects the melting point of ice. Different amounts of salt were dissolved in water and then frozen to a temperature of -15°C. The ice was then crushed and placed in a filter funnel and the temperature noted as soon as the ice began to produce drips of water. The results are shown below.

Amount of salt (g)	0	5	10	15	20	25
Melting point of ice (°C)	0	-1	-3	-2	-10	-13

(a)   Name three factors that must be carefully controlled in order to make this a fair test.

1 _____

2 _____

3 _____

(b)   Which one of these results looks wrong?

_____

(c)   What conclusion can you draw from this investigation?

_____

(d)   Name one practical application of this conclusion that is used regularly in winter in this country.

_____

Maximum 6 marks

5a

3 marks

5b

1 mark

5c

1 mark

5d

1 mark

6.   (a)(i) Acids and alkalis are often called 'chemical opposites'. Complete the following word equation to show what is produced when an acid is added to an alkali.

acid + alkali ⟶ _____ + _____

6ai
1 mark

(ii)   Write a word equation to show an example of a reaction between an acid and an alkali.

_____

6aii
1 mark

(iii) If the acid and alkali completely 'cancel each other out' so that the resulting solution is neutral, what will the pH be?

_____

6aiii
1 mark

(b)   A wasp sting can be treated by applying vinegar to it. What does this tell you about the pH of a wasp sting?

_____

6b
1 mark

(c)(i) Acids react with metal carbonates. Complete the following word equation to show what is produced.

acid + metal carbonate ⟶ _____ + _____ + _____

6ci
1 mark

(ii)   Write down a word equation to show an example of a reaction between an acid and a metal carbonate.

_____

6cii
1 mark

Maximum 6 marks

7. A simple balance can be made like the one shown below.

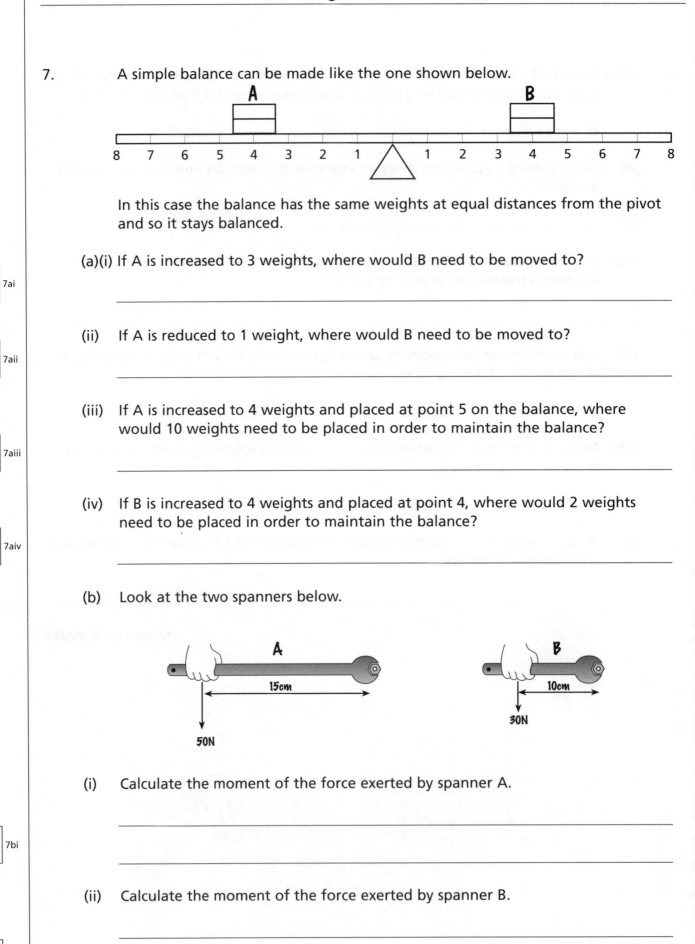

In this case the balance has the same weights at equal distances from the pivot and so it stays balanced.

(a)(i) If A is increased to 3 weights, where would B need to be moved to?

_____

7ai

1 mark

(ii) If A is reduced to 1 weight, where would B need to be moved to?

_____

7aii

1 mark

(iii) If A is increased to 4 weights and placed at point 5 on the balance, where would 10 weights need to be placed in order to maintain the balance?

_____

7aiii

1 mark

(iv) If B is increased to 4 weights and placed at point 4, where would 2 weights need to be placed in order to maintain the balance?

_____

7aiv

1 mark

(b) Look at the two spanners below.

(i) Calculate the moment of the force exerted by spanner A.

_____

_____

7bi

1 mark

(ii) Calculate the moment of the force exerted by spanner B.

_____

_____

7bii

1 mark

Maximum 6 marks

8. (a) Energy can exist in many forms. List three common forms of energy.

    1 _____

    2 _____

    3 _____

8a

3 marks

(b) Coal, oil and gas can be used to produce electricity. Rearrange the following statements to show the order of the process.

    A | Turbines turn the generator | **B** | Boiling water turns to steam |

    C | Heat from burning fuel is used to boil water | **D** | Steam turns the turbines |

    E | Generator produces electricity |

    ☐ ⟶ ☐ ⟶ ☐ ⟶ ☐ ⟶ ☐

8b

2 marks

(c) What is the original source of most energy resources?

    _____

8c

1 mark

Maximum 6 marks

9. Pupils were investigating the passage of light through a glass block. They set up the apparatus as shown below.

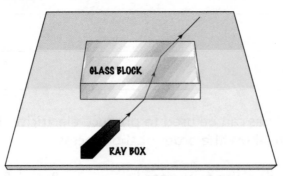

(a) Complete the following diagrams to show how a light ray would pass through the glass block.

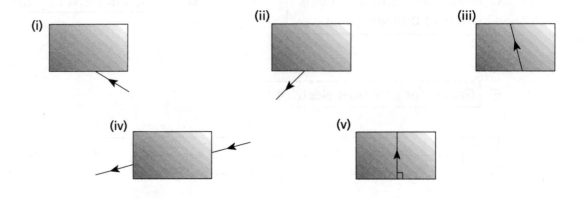

(b) When light passes from one transparent material to another it can change direction. What is the name given to this effect?

_____

Maximum 6 marks

9a

5 marks

9b

1 mark

10. (a) Draw 4 lines between the boxes below to link each word to the correct definition.

producer		an animal which eats both plants and animals
consumer		a green plant at the start of the food chain
omnivore		an animal that eats other animals
carnivore		all animals in the food chain

10a
2 marks

(b) Look at the food web below.

(i) Write down a food chain from the web that contains 4 organisms.

_____ → _____ → _____ → _____

10bi
1 mark

(ii) Write down the names of two secondary consumers

1 _____

2 _____

10bii
1 mark

(iii) Write down the name of a herbivore which eats two different producers.

_____

10biii
1 mark

(c) An insecticide is used on rose bushes in a particular area. Why could this cause problems for the hawk?

_____

10c
1 mark

Maximum 6 marks

11.   Paul and Joanne investigated the effects of nitrogen, in the form of nitrates, on plant growth. They watered 5 trays of seedlings on alternate days with different concentrations of nitrate fertiliser.

(a)   Name three factors which would need to be controlled in order to make this a fair test.

1 _____

2 _____

3 _____

11a
3 marks

(b)   How are nitrates absorbed from the soil?

_____

11b
1 mark

(c)   Name one other essential mineral for healthy plant growth.

_____

11c
1 mark

(d)   Explain why the Sundew, which is an insect-catching plant, can survive in areas where there are low nitrate levels in the soil.

_____

11d
1 mark

                                                        Maximum 6 marks

12. There are many ways to separate different substances. The diagrams below show different sets of equipment that can often be used.

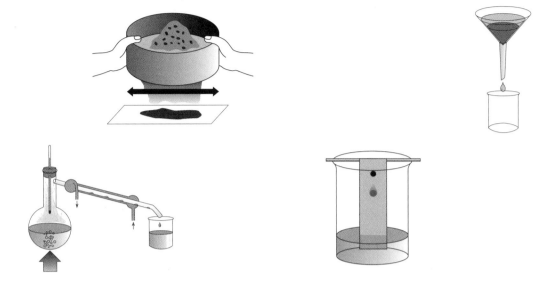

(a)(i) How would you separate a mixture of peas and rice?

_____

12ai

1 mark

(ii) How would you separate the pigments in a drop of water-soluble paint?

_____

12aii

1 mark

(iii) How would you separate ethanol from a mixture of ethanol and water?

_____

12aiii

1 mark

(b) Describe the process you would use to extract salt from a mixture of gravel, sand and salt.

_____

_____

_____

_____

12b

3 marks

Maximum 6 marks

13. (a) Describe two ways in which rocks at the surface of the Earth can be weathered.

1 _____

_____

2 _____

_____

13a
2 marks

(b) Igneous rock may be changed back into sedimentary rock by a process which involves four stages. Put the four stages shown below into their correct order.

A Deposition   B Transport   C Weathering   D Burial

13b
1 mark

(c) Name two key factors that are responsible for changing sedimentary rock into metamorphic rock.

1 _____

2 _____

13c
2 marks

(d) Describe one feature of igneous rock which has cooled quickly on or near the surface of the Earth.

_____

13d
1 mark

Maximum 6 marks

14. The following data was produced in an investigation into how the length of a guitar string affects the pitch of the sound it produces.

Length of string (cm)	60	50	40	30	20
Pitch of sound (Hz)	200	240	300	400	600

(a) Draw a graph to show the data.

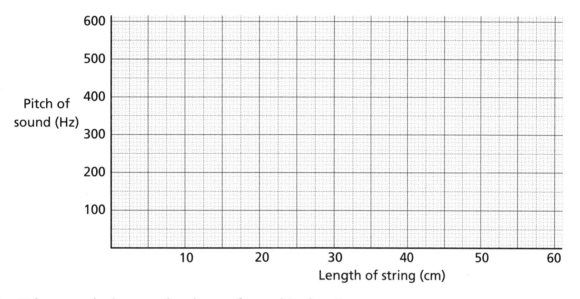

14a
1 mark

(b) What conclusion can be drawn from this data?

_____

_____

14b
1 mark

(c) Use your graph to answer the following questions.
(i) What is the pitch of the sound if the length of the string is 35cm?

_____

14ci
1 mark

(ii) What length of string would give a sound of pitch 520Hz?

_____

14cii
1 mark

(d) Name two factors that would need to be kept the same in order to make this a fair test.

1 _____

2 _____

14d
2 marks

Maximum 6 marks

15. The Earth is a planet in the solar system.

(a) Name two planets which are nearer to the Sun than Earth is.

1 _____

2 _____

15a
2 marks

(b) In general, what can be said about a planet's distance from the Sun in relation to the length of time it takes to complete an orbit?

_____

_____

15b
1 mark

(c) What keeps the planets in their orbits?

_____

15c
1 mark

(d) What are the names of the two largest planets?

1 _____

2 _____

15d
2 marks

Maximum 6 marks

Lonsdale

Our Student Workbook matches the Revision Guide page for page and provides great reinforcement and excellent homework material.